THE AUTHORITY

FRACTURED WORLDS

GODHEAD

WRITER — ROBBIE MORRISON   PENCILER — DWAYNE TURNER

INKER — SAL REGLA   COLORIST — DAVID BARON #6, WS/FX #7-9

LETTERS — JARED K. FLETCHER #6-8, PHIL BALSMAN #9

FRACTURED WORLD

WRITER — ROBBIE MORRISON   PENCILER — DWAYNE TURNER

INKER — SAL REGLA   COLORIST — DAVID BARON #10-11, WS/FX #12-13

LETTERS — PHIL BALSMAN

THE AUTHORITY: FRACTURED WORLDS published by WildStorm Productions, 888 Prospect St. #240, La Jolla, CA 92037. Compilation copyright © 2005 WildStorm Productions, an imprint of DC Comics. All Rights Reserved. WildStorm Universe Series, The Authority, all characters, the distinctive likenesses thereof and all related elements are trademarks of DC Comics. Originally published in single magazine form as THE AUTHORITY: VOLUME 2 #6-14 © 2003, 2004 DC Comics.

The stories, characters, and incidents mentioned in this magazine are entirely fictional. Printed on recyclable paper. WildStorm does not read or accept unsolicited submissions of ideas, stories or artwork. Printed in Canada.

DC Comics, a Warner Bros. Entertainment Company.

STREET LIFE

WRITER – ROBBIE MORRISON   PENCILER – WHILCE PORTACIO

INKER – SAL REGLA   COLORIST – WILDSTORM FX   LETTERS – PHIL BALSMAN

DESIGN– LARRY BERRY

THE AUTHORITY CREATED BY WARREN ELLIS AND BRYAN HITCH

GODHEAD

BOOK 1 OF 4

GODHEAD

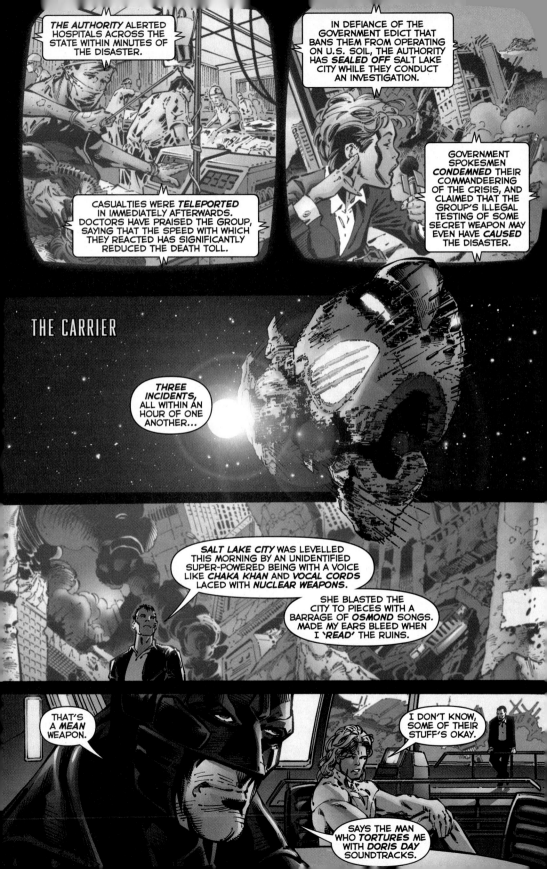

JOHN CLAY FOUNDED THE TRANSCENDENCE MOVEMENT AFTER HIS FILM CAREER HIT THE SKIDS BIG-TIME.

HE PROMOTES THE BELIEF THAT *EVERYONE* IS CAPABLE OF BECOMING SUPER-HUMAN. ALL YOU HAVE TO DO IS FOLLOW HIS TEACHINGS AND SIGN *25%* OF YOUR INCOME BEFORE TAX OVER TO HIS CHURCH.

INCREDIBLY ENOUGH, TRANSCENDENCE HAS BECOME THE WORLD'S FASTEST GROWING RELIGION, WITH OVER *13 MILLION* DISCIPLES ACROSS THE GLOBE-- INCLUDING HIGHLY INFLUENTIAL *POLITICIANS, A-LIST CELEBRITIES* AND *EVEN SUPERHUMANS.*

HIS LATEST DVD FEATURES THIS RATHER *FLATTERING* FOOTAGE OF US.

ONE PHOTO-SHOOT I *DON'T* REMEMBER TURNING UP FOR.

SO NOT ONLY IS CLAY TRYING TO OUTDO *JIM JONES* IN THE CULT STAKES...

IT LOOKS LIKE HE'S ALSO OUT TO *DESTROY* EVERY OTHER RELIGION IN AN ATTEMPT TO BOOST HIS OWN CONGREGATION.

THEN, LET'S GO GIVE THE SONUVABITCH A *SERMON* HE WON'T FORGET.

HOW WELL DO YOU THINK YOU'LL PREACH WITH HALF OF *LOS ANGELES* SHOVED DOWN YOUR THROAT, REVEREND?

AAAIIIEEEE!

ATTITUDE, ANGIE, THAT'S *ALWAYS* BEEN OUR BIGGEST PROBLEM.

WE DIDN'T *THINK* WE WERE RIGHT, WE *KNEW* WE WERE RIGHT. WE NEVER EVEN *CONSIDERED* THE OTHER OPTIONS. THE REVEREND ISN'T OUR ENEMY. HE'S OUR *SAVIOR!*

A-ANGIE... GET AWAY... GET...

THE *FUCK* YOU DOIN' HANGIN' AROUND WITH THIS *SHOELESS WONDER,* LADY?

YOU NEED SOME *ANIMAL MAGNETISM* IN YOUR LIFE!

NOW THEN, WHERE WERE...?

HMPH!

THE CARRIER
JUNCTION ROOM

DR. FELIX

WHOA THERE! LET ME RECAP FOR ANY VIEWERS WHO'VE JUST JOINED US...

I'M HERE WITH *CARDINAL*... WELL, SOME FOLKS MIGHT WANT TO CALL YOU *JUDAS* WHEN THEY HEAR WHAT YOU'VE GOT TO SAY ABOUT *YOUR ORDER*.

NO MATTER HOW *HOLY* AND *NOBLE* AND *IDEALISTIC* THEIR ORIGINS, *ALL* RELIGIOUS INSTITUTIONS BECOME LITTLE MORE THAN *TRADEMARKS* AND *CORPORATE LOGOS*...

COMMERCIAL ENTITIES THAT *EXPLOIT* THE FAITH OF THEIR FOLLOWERS, PREYING ON DOUBTS AND FEARS, ON OUR *NEED* TO BELIEVE IN SOMETHING *MORE* THAN THE CRUEL WORLD AROUND US.

YESTERDAY, I HAD AN AUDIENCE WITH THE *REVEREND JOHN CLAY*, A REMARKABLE MAN WHO SHOWED ME THAT IF WE WANT TO FIND SPIRITUAL ENLIGHTENMENT, IF WE WANT TO FIND GOD, THEN WE HAVE TO SEARCH *WITHIN OURSELVES*.

TODAY, I'M HERE TO ANNOUNCE MY *CONVERSION* TO THE *CHURCH* OF *TRANSCENDENCE*--THE TRUE RELIGION OF THE 21ST CENTURY!

ALL YOU HAVE TO DO IS BREAK *FREE* FROM A *LIFETIME* OF INDOCTRINATION!

ALL YOU HAVE TO DO IS *TRANSCEND*!

IF I CAN DO IT, ANYONE CAN DO IT!

YOU'RE *AMAZING*, LOLA. CHARTERING A JET TO FLY US ALL AROUND AFRICA LIKE THAT WAS *SELFLESS* AND...

DON'T WORRY, BABY, THEY'RE *PAYIN'* FOR IT!

WHAT? *WHO?*

DUH! THE GOVERNMENTS OF THE COUNTRIES WE JUST VISITED!

BUT...HALF THOSE NATIONS HAVE BEEN *BANKRUPTED* BY CIVIL WAR! THE OTHERS ARE *CRIPPLED* WITH DEBT REPAYMENTS...

SHOULDN'T THEY *BUY* WHAT THEY CAN'T *AFFORD* THEN, SHOULD THEY?

IT'S NOT THAT I DON'T *FEEL* THEIR PAIN, BUT *I* WASN'T BORN WITH NO SILVER SPOON IN MY MOUTH NEITHER.

I GOT WHERE I AM TODAY BY *HARD WORK* AND *BUSTIN'* MY ASS. THEY CAN DO THE *SAME.*

NOT EVERYONE'S GOT AN *ASS* LIKE YOURS!

DAMN *RIGHT* THEY DON'T! *"REAR OF THE YEAR"* FIVE TIMES RUNNING! AIN'T NO *ASS* WON IT THAT MUCH!

SPEAKING OF *ASSES*, YOUR *SKINNY* CHEEKS COULD DO WITH A LITTLE BEEFIN' UP. I'M GONNA PUT YOU ON AN *EXERCISE* PROGRAM.

LOLA, I COULD'VE *MAGICKED* US THERE. *EVERYBODY!* YOUR ENTIRE ENTOURAGE...

WHAT KIND OF ENTRANCE IS THAT? THEY WANT *GLITZ* AND *GLAMOUR*, *SEXY* AND *SASSY*, PLANES AND *LIMOS!*

ALL THOSE *POOR LITTLE BLACK BABIES* OUT THERE? I'M THEIR ROLE *MODEL*... THEIR *INSPIRATION!* THEY *NEED* ME TO LOOK UP TO!

THE CARRIER

SHIFTING RANDOMLY THROUGH REALITIES TO EVADE DETECTION BY HOSTILE FORCES.

ONE OF US.

ONE OF US.

ONE OF US.

THAT'S MORE OR LESS IT, SWIFT. LAST ESTIMATE, *70%* OF THE POPULATION HAS ALREADY CONVERTED TO TRANSCENDENCE.

AT THIS RATE, WE'LL *ALL* BE SINGING CLAY'S PRAISES IN ANOTHER *TWO* WEEKS!

NEVER UNDERESTIMATE THE *GULLIBILITY* OF THE HUMAN RACE, HUH.

THERE'S A LITTLE MORE TO IT THAN THAT, APOLLO.

THERE'VE ALWAYS BEEN RUMORS IN HOLLYWOOD ABOUT CLAY POSSESSING SOME SORT OF *PSIONIC SKILL* OR *CHARM*, A SUPERNATURAL ABILITY TO *INFLUENCE* PEOPLE.

WATCH *THIS*...

FOOTAGE FROM A CHURCH OF TRANSCENDENCE *MASS CONVERSION* CEREMONY.

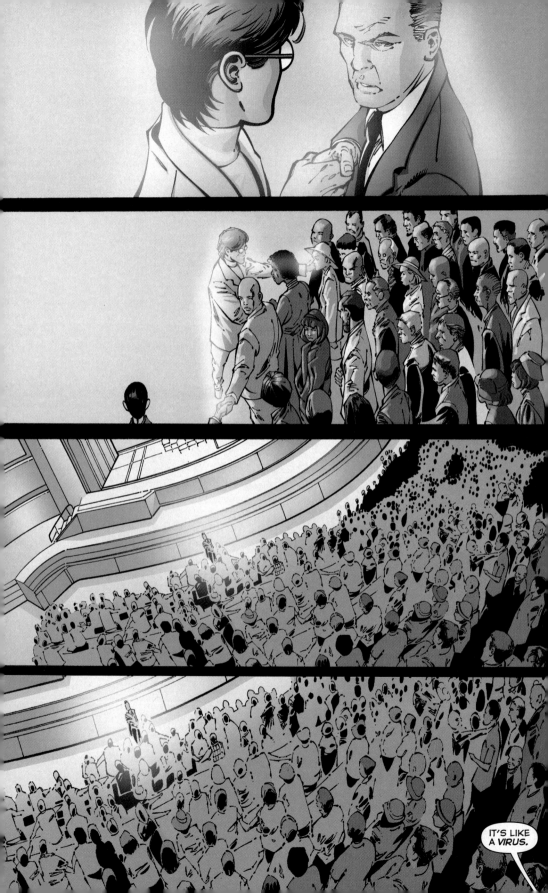

A *NEURAL VIRUS* THAT MANIPULATES MINDS AND IS SPREAD THROUGH PHYSICAL CONTACT--CLAY'S "*LAYING ON OF HANDS*".

CLAY'S POWER HIJACKS THE *NUCLEUS ACCUMBENS* REGION OF THE BRAIN...

... A CROSSROADS BETWEEN THE *DOPAMINE SYSTEM,* WHICH MEDIATES THE PLEASURE RESPONSE TO FACTORS SUCH AS DRUGS OR FOOD, AND THE *LIMBIC SYSTEM,* WHICH HELPS FORM MOTIVATION AND MEMORY.

WE LIVE IN A *SENTIENT SHIFTSHIP* THAT TRAVERSES *REALITIES* AND YOU'RE FLUMMOXED BY A *TEENY* BIT OF SCIENCE LIKE THAT?

HE FIRES UP THEIR BRAINS TO TURN THEM INTO *ZOMBIFIED RELIGIOUS FANATICS* WITH HIMSELF AS *JESUS.*

BETTER?

CLAY TOUCHES SOMEONE AND THEY'RE IMMEDIATELY CONVERTED TO HIS WAY OF THINKING. THEY TOUCH FRIENDS, FAMILY, ANYONE AND *BANG!* IT'S LIKE A *DOMINO EFFECT.*

CAN YOU REVERSE THE BRAINWASHING?

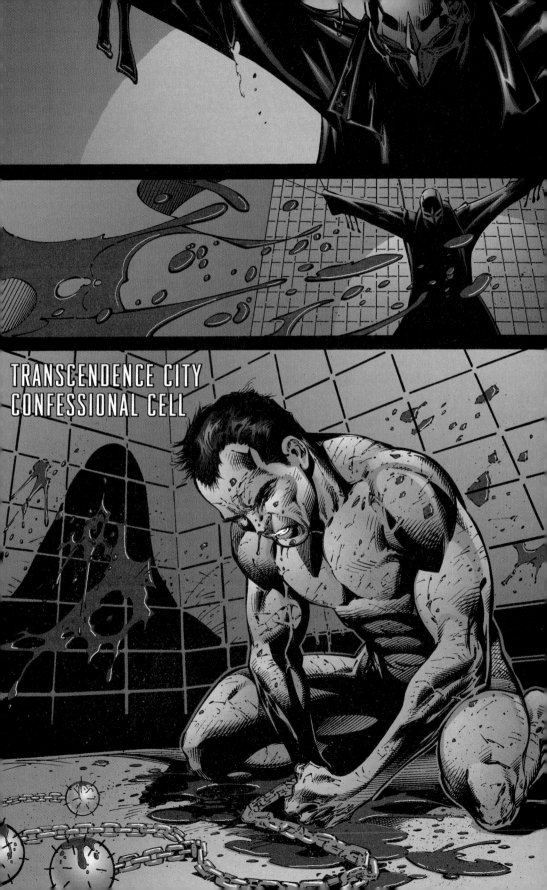

TRANSCENDENCE CITY
CONFESSIONAL CELL

IT CAN GET *LONELY* AT THE TOP. BUT I DON'T NEED TO TELL YOU THAT, DO I?

YOU'RE THE LEADING ACTRESSES OF YOUR DAY. YOU KNOW ALL ABOUT THE *PRESSURES* OF *FAME.*

PRESS INTRUSIONS. STALKERS. THE DIRECTOR WHO SAYS HE WON'T SHOOT YOU NUDE, THEN *PLASTERS* YOUR ASS ALL ACROSS THE SCREEN. ACTOR BOYFRIENDS WHO DO THE DIRTY AND RUN OFF WITH LAPDANCERS!

ALTERNATE 121

A SOLAR SYSTEM POWERED BY TWIN SUNS.

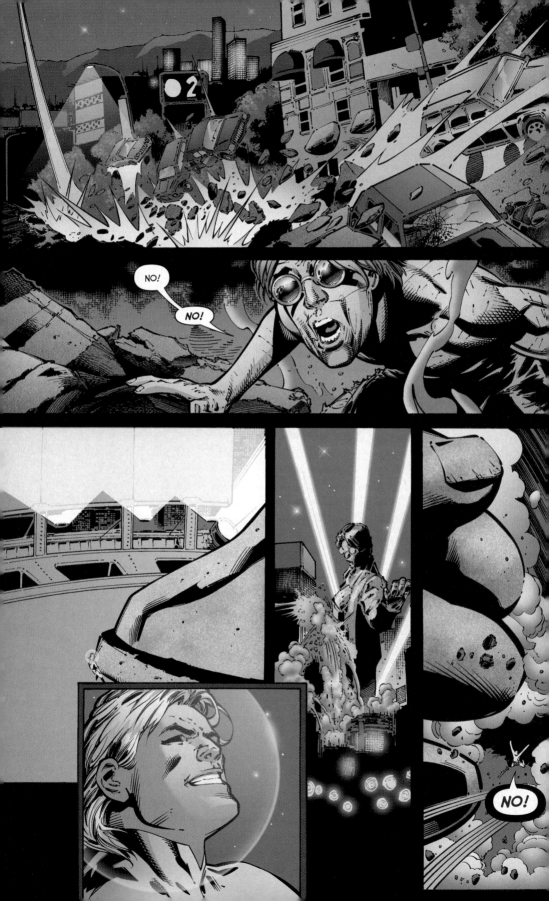

CHURCH OF TRANSCENDENCE CELEBRITY CENTER

...YOU WERE A LOT MORE *OPEN-MINDED* BEFORE YOU FOUND RELIGION.

YOU KNOW, JACK...

OR RATHER, BEFORE *IT* FOUND YOU.

I'VE JUST INFECTED YOUR BLOODSTREAM WITH *NANOTECH NEURAL STIMULANTS* TO BREAK THE *PSIONIC HOLD* CLAY HAS OVER YOUR MIND.

I ALSO BROUGHT ALONG A LITTLE BAG OF *TRICKS* FROM YOUR PRIVATE ARSENAL.

HOW'RE YOU FEELING?

IT'S THE SAME IN EVERY MAJOR CITY.

MASSIVE CROWDS GATHERED AROUND THE CHURCH OF TRANSCENDENCE'S MULTI-MEDIA TEMPLES.

I THOUGHT YOU SAID YOU RELINQUISHED CONTROL OF THE PSIONIC HOLD CLAY HAD OVER THEM?

I DID. THE MAJORITY RETURNED TO THE FAITHS THEY FOLLOWED BEFORE THE REVEREND FORCED HIMSELF UPON THEM. BUT THE ONES OUT THERE...

THEY WANT TO BELIEVE.

IN WHAT?

THE GREATER GOOD. A HIGHER AUTHORITY.

EVERYTHING WE STAND FOR.

AND THAT GIVES YOU THE RIGHT TO START COMING ON LIKE OUR OWN PERSONAL JESUS?

NONE OF US ARE EXACTLY COMFORTABLE WITH THIS, DOCTOR.

I AM.

WE'VE BEEN BEATING OUR HEADS AGAINST THE WALL FOR LONG ENOUGH.

IT'S TIME WE REALIZED THERE'S MORE THAN ONE WAY TO CHANGE THE WORLD.

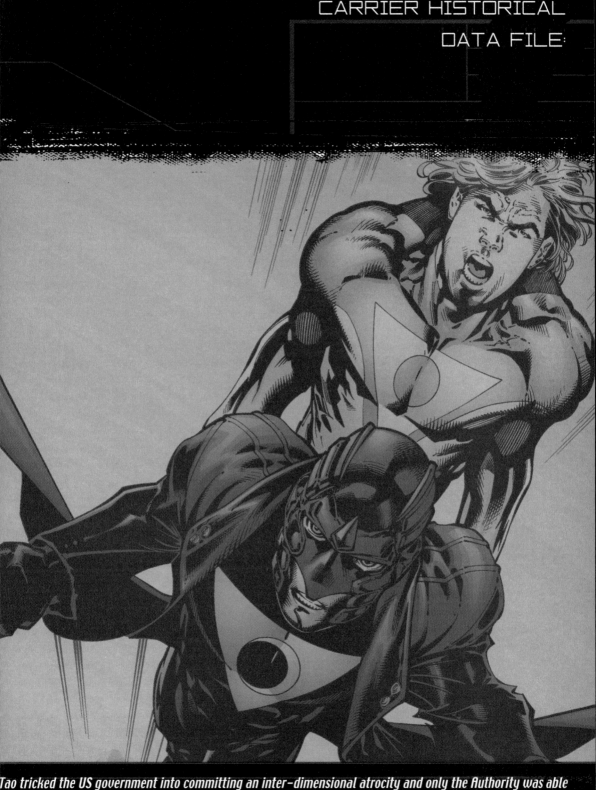

Tao tricked the US government into committing an inter-dimensional atrocity and only the Authority was able to intervene and save the planet. Unaware of Tao's involvement, they were forced to take drastic measures to prevent this from ever happening again by usurping the American government and taking charge themselves. But their actions sent shock waves through the entire planet and even forced Stormwatch: Team Achilles and the Wildcats to question the Authority's decision. Whether or not these super teams co-exist under the new status quo is yet to be determined.

See Coup D' Etat trade paperback for further details.

CHAPTER TWO

FRACTURED WORLD

FRACTURED WORLD

BOOK 1 OF 4

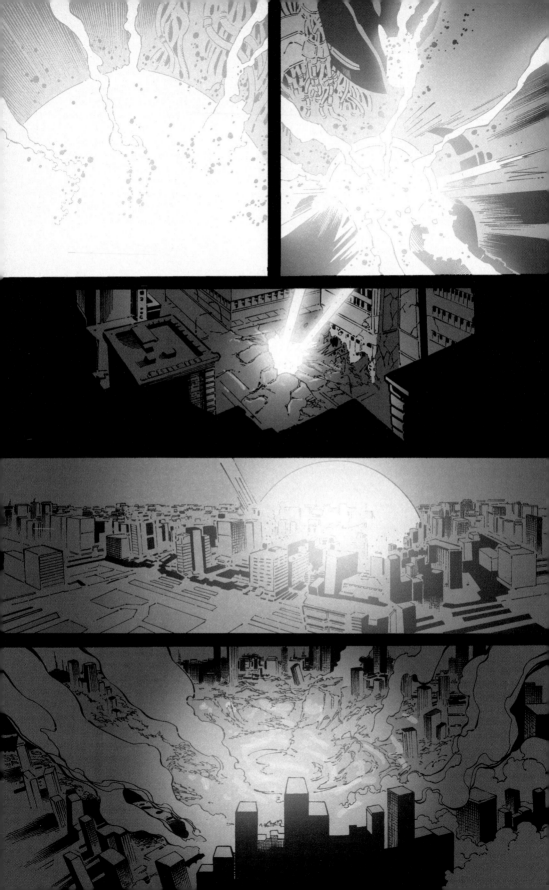

DALLAS, TEXAS

GENTLEMEN, WE GAVE YOU THE CHANCE TO HELP BUILD SOMETHING *WORTHWHILE* AND YOU *THREW* IT BACK IN OUR FACES.

SO, AS OF NOW, YOU JUST *LOST* THE ELEMENT OF *CHOICE.*

STARTING IMMEDIATELY, YOU WILL CHANNEL *12.5%* OF YOUR *GROSS* PROFITS INTO RESEARCH AND DEVELOPMENT PROGRAMS FOR ENVIRONMENTALLY-FRIENDLY FORMS OF ENERGY.

ANY ARGUMENTS, AND THAT FIGURE WILL BE INCREASED TO *15%.*

MISS LI MIN... SWIFTY...WHATEVER YOU WANT TO CALL YOURSELF...

YOU SEEM UNABLE TO GRASP THE SIMPLE FACT THAT *YOU* NEED US MORE THAN *WE* NEED YOU.

WE'RE THE POWER *BEHIND* THE POWER, SO TO SPEAK, SO YOU BEST *SNUGGLE UP* TO US.

DOCTOR.

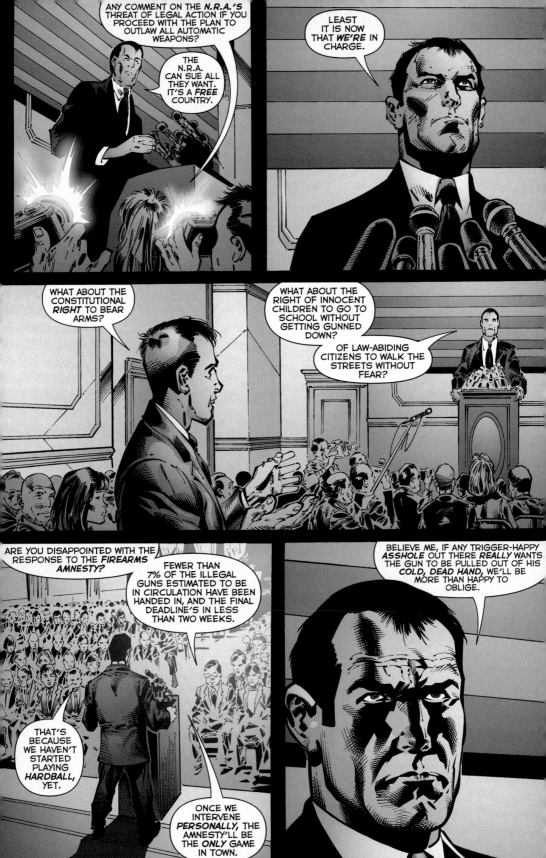

THIS ISN'T *"THE WEST WING,"* IT'S THE REAL WORLD.

WE PROMISED THAT OUR TERM IN OFFICE--IF YOU *INSIST* ON CALLING IT THAT--WOULD BE *A BULLSHIT-FREE* ZONE. WE'LL TELL IT LIKE IT *IS.*

MR. HAWKSMOOR, AS A POTENTIAL ROLE MODEL TO MILLIONS, DON'T YOU THINK YOU SHOULD ADOPT A MORE... *PRESIDENTIAL* TONE?

ANY TRUTH TO THE RUMORS THAT A WOMAN HAS COME FORWARD CLAIMING TO BE *JENNY QUANTUM'S* MOTHER?

NO COMMENT.

IS *THAT* AN EXAMPLE OF TELLING IT LIKE IT IS, JACK?

SIR, JENNY QUANTUM IS REPUTEDLY THE MOST *POWERFUL* SUPER-HUMAN ON THE PLANET.

DON'T WE *DESERVE* TO KNOW...?

I SAID, *NO* COMMENT.

WE'RE DONE.

QUESTION TIME'S OVER.

ANGIE'S MEETING WITH *THE LAWYERS* JUST NOW.

SHIT...

SAN FRANCISCO

THE LEGAL FIRM OF CHIREN & LOEB

OUT OF COMPASSION FOR MS. LEUNG'S LOSS, THE CHINESE GOVERNMENT HAS AGREED TO MEET ALL HER LEGAL COSTS IF YOU CHALLENGE HER RIGHT TO SEE HER DAUGHTER.

YEAH?

WE SAW A LOT OF CHINA'S *COMPASSION* WHEN WE LIBERATED *TIBET.*

I HOPE YOU'RE NOT GOING TO LET *PERSONAL PREJUDICE* COLOR YOUR JUDGEMENT, MS. SPICA.

AS A "*SUPERHERO,*" AREN'T YOU SWORN TO HELP THE LIKES OF MS. LEUNG? SHE IS THE *VICTIM* HERE...

DEALY PLAZA, DALLAS

DIDN'T KNOW WE WERE SO POPULAR...

WE'RE *NOT*.

HALF THE CROWD'S THROWING *BRICKS, BOTTLES* AND *ROTTEN VEGETABLES*. I'M MAGICALLY TURNING THEM INTO OBJECTS OF *AFFECTION*.

THE OTHER HALF ARE *CHURCH OF SHAMANISM* DISCIPLES, HERE TO *PRAISE* THEIR SPIRITUAL GUIDE AND MENTOR.

I LEAKED OUR ITINERARY TO *BOOST* THE CROWD NUMBERS.

ISN'T THAT A LITTLE *UNETHICAL?*

SHEN, WE OVERTHREW THE U.S. GOVERNMENT, TOOK CONTROL, THEN STARTED *STRANGLING* ALL THE BASTARDS IN THE WORLD WITH THE REINS OF POWER.

WE'RE *REWRITING* THE BOOK ON ETHICS--

URKHHHH!

JEROEN!

F-FRACTURES...

FRACTURES IN THE EARTH...

PARIS,
FRANCE

THE AUTHORITY SUCCESSFULLY SEALED THE RUPTURES, BUT HAS PLACED THE UNITED STATES ON A STATE OF ALERT, WARNING THAT FURTHER BREACHES COULD OCCUR AT ANY TIME.

OTHER NATIONS HAVE BEEN STRONGLY ADVISED TO DO LIKEWISE.

W.N.N

...JACK HAWKSMOOR ISSUED A BRIEF STATEMENT, PROMISING THAT THE AUTHORITY WILL DEVOTE ALL ITS POWER AND RESOURCES INTO INVESTIGATING AND ELIMINATING THE CAUSE OF THE DISASTERS.

W.N.N   BREAKING NEWS

BOTH REPUBLICAN AND DEMOCRATIC PARTY SPOKESMEN HAVE RAISED THE QUESTION OF HOW THE SUPERGROUP CAN POSSIBLY CONTINUE THE DAY-TO-DAY RUNNING OF THE COUNTRY, WHILE ENGAGED IN AN ENDEAVOUR OF THIS MAGNITUDE AND IMPORTANCE.

LAWYERS ACTING FOR MICHELLE LEUNG, THE WOMAN WHO CLAIMS TO BE JENNY QUANTUM'S MOTHER, HAVE DROPPED THEIR LEGAL ACTION FOLLOWING AN OUT-OF-COURT AGREEMENT, RUMORED TO GRANT HER ACCESS TO THE INFANT.

AUTHORITY MEMBERS APOLLO AND THE MIDNIGHTER FORMALLY ADOPTED THE INFANT THREE YEARS AGO, AND HAVE FOUGHT TO KEEP HER OUT OF THE SPOTLIGHT EVER...

W.N.N

THE CARRIER, EARTH ORBIT

AN HOUR AGO, EARTH EXPERIENCED A SERIES OF *FRACTURES* IN REALITY.

WE DID OUR BEST, AND SWIFT TELEPORTED AS MANY VICTIMS OUT OF THE DANGER ZONES AS POSSIBLE, BUT CASUALTIES STILL RUN INTO THE *THOUSANDS*.

THE CARRIER HELPED ME PINPOINT THE OTHER REALITIES THAT RIPPED INTO OURS THROUGH THE FRACTURES...

HIVE-MIND.

IN JOHANNESBURG, A RUPTURE OPENED UP INTO THE ATLANTIC OCEAN OF ALTERNATE 995, FLOODING THE CITY.

THE RIO FRACTURE OPENED A GATEWAY TO ALTERNATE 666, WHERE THE SUPERHEROES WERE SO *CLEAN-CUT* THAT THEY REFUSED TO KILL THEIR ENEMIES...

...AND GOT *SLAUGHTERED* FOR IT. EVERY SINGLE ONE OF THEM.

THE PARIS RUPTURE LED TO ALTERNATE 12, WHERE "OUR" GALAXY HAS REACHED THE END OF ITS LIFESPAN, AND THE SUN'S ABOUT TO TURN SUPERNOVA.

ALL HUMAN LIFE WAS *INCINERATED* DECADES AGO.

SINCE THE CRASH OF THE ALIEN SHIFTSHIP THAT DESTROYED FLORIDA AND FORCED US TO TAKE CHARGE OF AMERICA, THERE'VE BEEN DOZENS OF LOCAL INSTABILITIES WITHIN THE BLEED...

AS YET, WE HAVE NO IDEA WHAT CAUSED THESE RUPTURES-- OR WHETHER OR NOT TO EXPECT MORE.

...MOST WERE MINOR, AND HAVE BEEN CONTAINED BY THE EMERGENCY SERVICES OF THE COUNTRIES THEY AFFECTED.

THE FIRST OF THESE WAS REPORTED IN *HENAN PROVINCE, CHINA.* JACK'S THERE JUST NOW, CONDUCTING INVESTIGATIONS. WE'LL HOOK UP VIA THE HIVE-MIND.

THE CHINESE GOVERNMENT'S *OFFICIAL* EXPLANATION OF WHAT HAPPENED DOESN'T TIE WITH WHAT I'M READING FROM THE RUINS.

IT'S *FRAGMENTED...* *SEARED* WITH THE PAIN OF THE PEOPLE WHO DIED HERE, THE COMMUNITY THAT WAS DESTROYED...

THERE WAS SOME SORT OF UNDERGROUND COMPLEX BENEATH THE CITY...

USED FOR *INCARCERATION,* MAYBE *EXPERIMENTATION.*

SOMEONE OR SOMETHING *SUFFERED INCREDIBLY* DOWN HERE, HIDDEN AWAY FROM THE WORLD...

WHATEVER HAPPENED HERE DIDN'T COME FROM *OUTSIDE* OUR REALITY.

SWIFT, YOU'VE BEEN TOP OF BEIJING'S *"LEAST WANTED"* LIST SINCE TIBET.

HOW ABOUT PAYING *CHAIRMAN CHAN* A LITTLE VISIT?

HOW DID WE MISS THIS?

TOO BUSY CONGRATULATING OURSELVES, SMILING FOR THE FUCKING CAMERAS!

IT HAPPENED ON THE DAY OF THE COUP.

THERE WAS TOO MUCH GOING DOWN. NOBODY'S INFALLIBLE.

WE *HAVE* TO BE, JACK!

BEIJING, CHINA

THE SEAT OF POWER...

...SO TO SPEAK.

FROM *COMMUNISM* TO *CONSUMERISM* WITH ONE DROP OF YOUR PANTS, HUH, CHAIRMAN?

IT WASN'T
THE *MOTHER.*

WE CALLED
HER *"FRACTAL"* WHEN
WE REALIZED WHAT
SHE WAS...

*"JENNY
FRACTAL."*

THE WOMAN WHO CLAIMED TO BE JENNY'S MOTHER IS ACTUALLY HER SISTER-- HER *TWIN* SISTER!

CHINESE AGENTS PULLED HER UNHARMED FROM THE RUBBLE OF SINGAPORE GENERAL AFTER OUR BATTLE WITH *KRIGSTEIN'S* SUPER-SOLDIERS.

THERE'S SO MUCH WE DON'T KNOW ABOUT *JENNY SPARKS'* ORIGINS, OR HER *REINCARNATION* PROCESS...

WHETHER HER SPIRIT *HIJACKED* MICHELLE LEUNG'S WOMB, SHARING IT WITH AN ALREADY CONCEIVED CHILD, OR WHETHER *BOTH* TWINS WERE FORMED FROM JENNY'S ESSENCE ISN'T IMPORTANT *RIGHT* NOW.

BOTH KIDS POSSESS THE SAME *OFF-THE-SCALE* POWERS.

THE PROBLEM IS THE CHINESE BROUGHT THEIR JENNY UP A LITTLE DIFFERENTLY FROM US.

THEY IMMERSED HER IN AN ASSASSIN PROGRAM-- HYPER-LEARNING, KILLING TECHNIQUES, THE ART OF WAR. THEY INTENDED TO CREATE A REMORSELESS, UNTHINKING SUPER-WEAPON LOYAL ONLY TO THEM.

WASHINGTON, DC.

FRACTURED WORLD
BOOK 4 OF 4

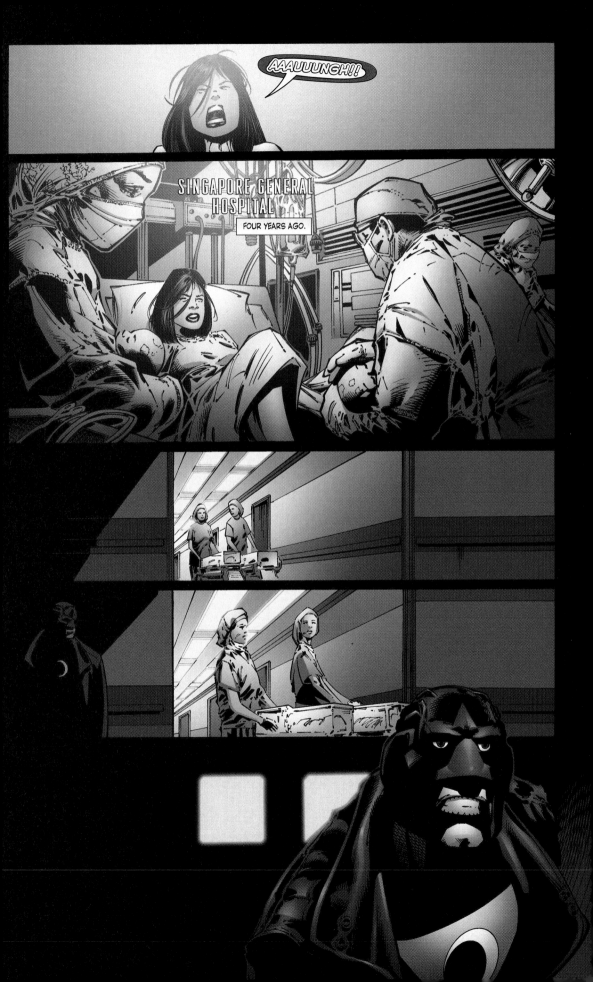

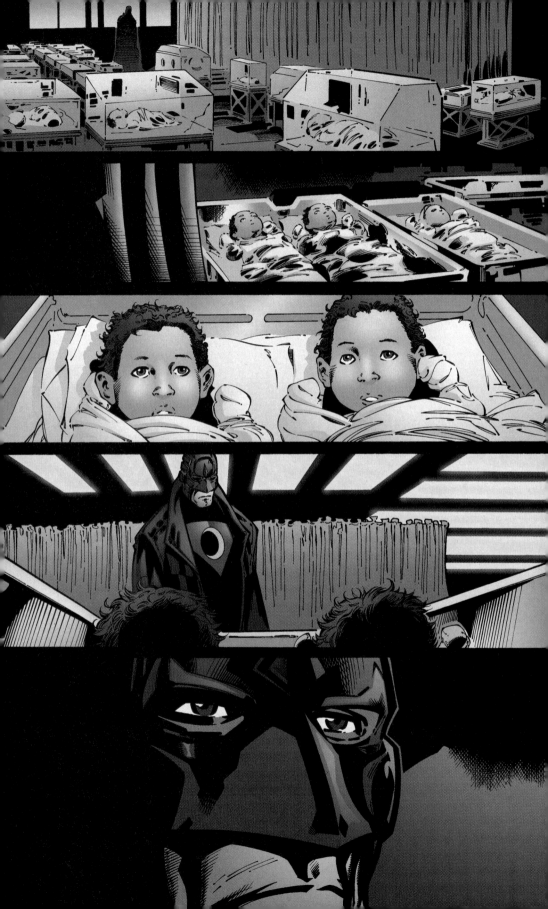

IT WORKED. JENNY TRANSFERRED HER CONSCIOUSNESS INTO FRACTAL'S BODY AT THE EXACT MOMENT OF HER DEATH.

THEY WERE BOTH THE REINCARNATION OF *JENNY SPARKS*, IDENTICAL IN ALMOST EVERY RESPECT, SO THE NATURAL ORDER--IF YOU WANT TO CALL IT THAT--IS RESTORED.

AND WE GET OUR JENNY BACK.

GO TO HER.

I CAN'T.

I CAN'T LOOK HER IN THE EYE AFTER WHAT I DID TONIGHT.

FRACTAL... SHE WASN'T *EVIL.* NOT *THEN.*

IT WAS *US* THAT DID THAT TO HER. *THIS WORLD...*

WE'RE *CHANGING* THE WORLD, MIDNIGHTER.

THE CARRIER

EARTH ORBIT.

WE'RE TAKING JENNY ON A LITTLE TRIP.

WE'RE GOING TO SHOW HER ALL THE *GOOD* THINGS ABOUT THE WORLD, LET HER KNOW *WHY* WE DO WHAT WE DO.

WE'RE STARTING IN *AFRICA*, *HIGH-DIVING* OFF *VICTORIA FALLS*.

SEE WHICH ONE OF US CAN HIT THE WATER FIRST.

BET IT'S *APOLLO!*

HEY, THE PAIR OF YOU MIGHT BE ABLE TO FLY, BUT I CAN *FALL* PRETTY DAMN FAST.

CHAPTER THREE

STREET LIFE

STREET LIFE

JACK HAWKSMOOR

WATCHING THE WORLD GO BY.

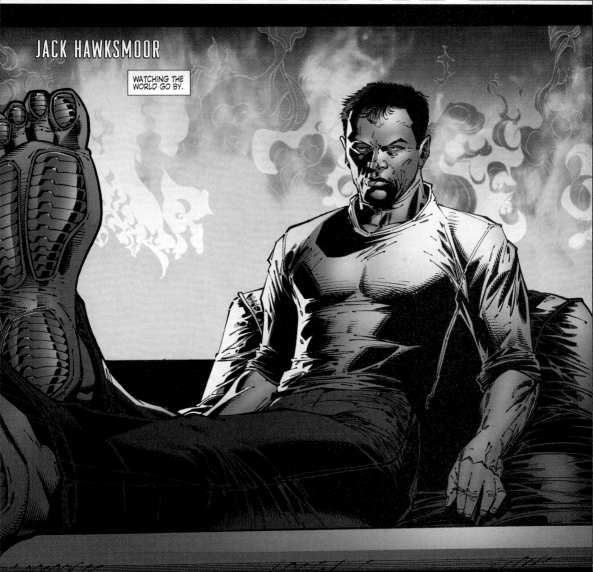

THE CARRIER COMMUNICATIONS ROOM

INDIAN-PAKISTANI RELATIONS FELL TO A DANGEROUS NEW LOW AFTER NEW DELHI BLAMED ISLAMABAD FOR THE MASSACRE IN KASHMIR EARLIER THIS WEEK.

IN A SHOW OF STRENGTH, INDIA TEST-FIRED A NUCLEAR-CAPABLE MISSILE EARLY THIS MORNING. PAKISTAN FOLLOWED SUIT A FEW HOURS LATER. BOTH MISSILES WERE INTERCEPTED AND DESTROYED BY MEMBERS OF THE AUTHORITY.

--UNPRECEDENTED EXPLOSION OF STATE-SPONSORED VIOLENCE ERUPTED AMIDST CHARGES OF VOTE-RIGGING ON A MASSIVE--

--HIGH RISK OF EPIDEMIC DISEASE IF--

AN ISRAELI ARMY UNDERCOVER SQUAD SHOT DEAD A TEN-YEAR-OLD GIRL IN BETHLEHEM LAST NIGHT IN WHAT THE MILITARY HAVE CALLED A "TRAGIC ACCIDENT."

FOLLOWING THE COUP D'ETAT, RUSSIA IMMEDIATELY PULLED OUT OF STRATEGIC ARMS CONTROL NEGOTIATIONS WITH THE UNITED STATES, REFUSING TO DEAL WITH WHAT THEY DESCRIBE AS AN ILLEGAL GOVERNMENT.

RUSSIAN PREMIER, VLADIMIR PUSHKIN: "CUTTING OUR WEAPONS CAPABILITY IN LIGHT OF THE AUTHORITY'S INCREASINGLY BELLIGERENT STANCE ON WORLD AFFAIRS WOULD BE TANTAMOUNT TO SUICIDE."

--NEW HUMAN RIGHTS EMERGENCY--

THE N.Y.P.D. TODAY LAUNCHED A HOMICIDE INVESTIGATION...

...FOLLOWING THE KILLING OF A WOMAN IN THE HELL'S KITCHEN DISTRICT OF THE CITY.

THE BODY OF KATHERINE BRADSHAW, A 34-YEAR-OLD SOCIAL WORKER, WAS DISCOVERED IN HER APARTMENT AFTER WORK COLLEAGUES ALERTED...

HELL'S KITCHEN

NEW YORK CITY

EARTH ORBIT.

"TYLER KING, 31.

"HISTORY OF EXTREME VIOLENCE FROM AGE 14, WHEN HE CUT UP A DEALER'S FACE WITH A BROKEN BOTTLE AND STOLE HIS TAKINGS. HE'S BEEN IN AND OUT OF CUSTODY EVER SINCE.

"BY HIS EARLY TWENTIES, HE WAS A MAJOR PLAYER IN THE HELL'S KITCHEN UNDERWORLD--DRUGS, PROSTITUTION, GRAND THEFT AUTO.

EXPIRES 07-09-01

OVER THE YEARS, HIS PARTNERS AND RIVALS HAVE BEEN PICKED OFF ONE BY ONE, LEAVING HIM IN CHARGE.

CONSIDERING THE *SCALE* WE'RE WORKING ON THESE DAYS, JACK, DON'T YOU THINK THIS IS--

BENEATH US? MAYBE. MAYBE NOT.

YOU EVER WONDER IF THE *LITTLE* STUFF HAPPENS BECAUSE OF THE *BIG* STUFF, OR IF THE BIG STUFF HAPPENS BECAUSE OF THE LITTLE STUFF?

ALL THE TIME.

YOU *KNOW* IT'S NEVER AS *SIMPLE* AS THAT. ALL I'M SAYING IS THAT MAYBE WE SHOULD STAY *FOCUSED.*

I *AM* FOCUSED, ANGIE.

HEY, TY!

YOU FIGURE IT'S WISE CRUISING AROUND WITH THIS GUY AFTER YOU?

AIN'T NOBODY GONNA FREAK ME OUT ON MY OWN TURF. AMOUNT OF FIREPOWER WE GOT? *BRING IT ON*, THAT'S WHAT I SAY.

BRING IT ON, MOTHER --

FFDD-MMPPHH

SHIT! TY, SOMEONE'S ON THE ROOF! THE ROAD'S GOIN' CRAZY! I CAN'T...

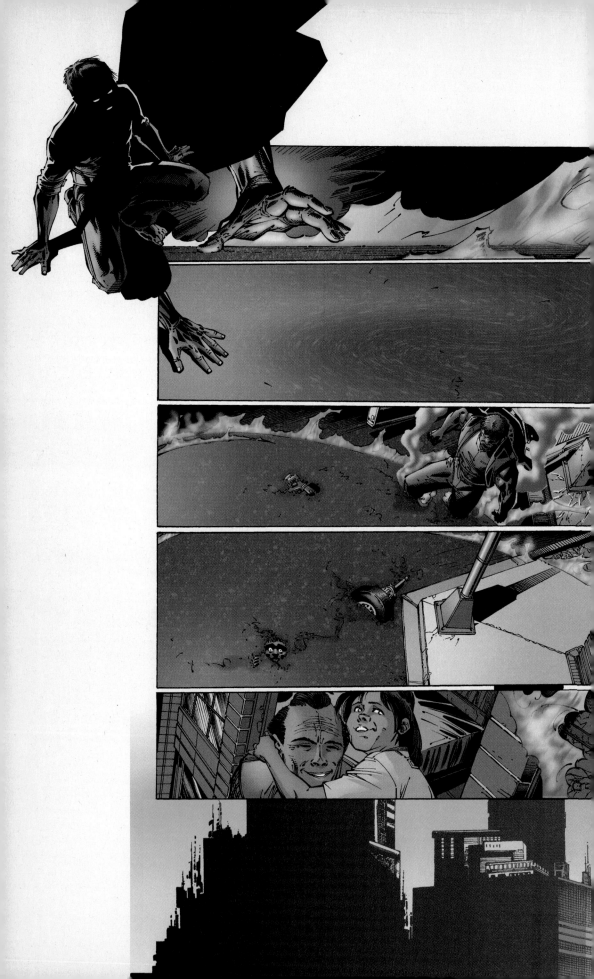

THE AUTHORITY
BOOKS 1-5

VARIOUS WRITERS & ARTISTS

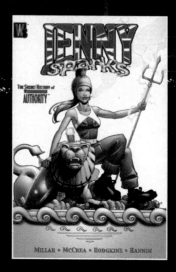

JENNY SPARKS:
SECRET HISTORY OF
THE AUTHORITY

MILLAR/MCCREA/HODGKINS

COUP D'ETAT

VARIOUS WRITERS
AND ARTISTS

21 DOWN
THE CONDUIT

PAMIOTTI/GRAY/SAIZ

SLEEPER
BOOKS 1 & 2

BRUBAKER/PHILLIPS

WILDCATS VERSION 3.0
BOOKS 1 & 2

CASEY/NGUYEN/FRIEND

SEARCH THE GRAPHIC-NOVELS SECTION OF
WILDSTORM.COM FOR ART AND INFO ON EVERY ONE
OF OUR HUNDREDS OF BOOKS!

TO FIND MORE COLLECTED EDITIONS AND MONTHLY COMIC BOOKS FROM WILDSTORM
AND DC COMICS, CALL 1-888-COMIC BOOK FOR THE NEAREST COMICS SHOP OR
GO TO YOUR LOCAL BOOK STORE.